Decodable Reader Library

Unit 3 Let's Connect!

Contents

Jane and Wade

by Maryann Dobeck

illustrated by Hector Borlasca

Today is a big pet show.
It is at the Tate School.
It's in Miss Hale's class.

Gale came with pet fish.
Shane came with his dog.
Dave came with a snake!

Jane came with a frog.
"His name is Wade,"
said Jane.
"Wade is the best pet."

4

"Why?" Gale asked.
Just then Wade jumped up.
Jane yelled, "Get Wade!"
But Jane was too late.

Jane's frog got away!
Where did Wade end up?
He jumped in the fish tank.
What a way to have fun!

6

Slap Hello!

by Ana Ruiz

What ways can we tell hello?
Let's all stand and wave.
Let's pull off hats.
Let's snap and clap hands.

Tim can walk up to Gramps.
Gramps has a big grin.
Gramps could wave a hand.
But Gramps pats and hugs.

Will the men slap backs?
No, the men will just grin
and clasp hands.
Then they will chat.

"Stop and spend a little
time with me!"
The pals will not hug and kiss.
But they will shake hands.

Kiss, kiss, kiss!
Step up and get a quick hug.
Oh, Mom has a big, big grin!

Such a Grand Day!

by Anna Keyes

The big sun is up at six.
People stretch in bed and
then get up.
Let's check in with them.

Whip up a batch of buns.
I wish I had a hot
baked bun. Yum!
Which one can I pick?

Kids can take care of a pet.
Dogs and cats get some
fresh water.
When will the pets get fed?

Kids chat in a bunch.
One boy and girl just
came on the bus.
Don't be late for class!

Kids check the lunch case.
Munch on fish and chips!
Grab a sandwich!

Get together and grin.
Play a game of chess.
Pitch and catch with
a pal.

The sun sets in the west.
I can see pink and red.
I had such fun today!

Job Time for the Pines

The Pines

by Liz Ray
illustrated by R. W. Alley

Mom and Dad must rest.

"Let's switch our jobs,"
Mike and Kim tell them.

"Fine," nod Mom and Dad.

"Would you like a snack?"
Mike asks Dad.

Dad takes a bite.
"This is not ripe!"

Mom rides Kim's bike.
"Your bike isn't my size,"
Mom tells Kim.
Kim smiles at Mom.

Dad must make Mike's bed.
"Let's make it line up,"
Dad tells Mike.
But Dad bumps the light.

Kim wipes up the suds.
"I must rest," she whines.

"It's time to switch back
again," smiles Mom.

A Trip Last Spring

by Olivia Clay
illustrated by Deborah Melmon

I am Jon.
I am looking at photos.
I think it is so much fun.

Here I am with Mom and Dad.
Last spring, we went on a
plane to see Pop Streck.
Pop Streck is Dad's dad.

This is Kim. Kim is five.
Kim has on a funny top.
It has stripes and dots!

This big, black dog is mine.
I call him Shag. Shag made
a splash in the mud.
I had to scrub him!

There is much more to see.
But it is time for bed.
How can I save this spot?
This string can save it!

It's Time for Fun

by Carol Lindeen

Take time off.
This is a big date.
Let's make it fun!

Let's take a bike ride.
I spot some striped flags.
How many can you spot?

A band is marching past.
We smile at this band.
Let's clap as they step.

I get together with pals.
We can chat and catch up.
I yell, "Let's play games!"

We can play a ball game.
Stand at the plate.
Take a big whack!

Let's make a big lunch.
I can pitch in and help.

I stretch out on my back.
I gaze up and think.
This was such fun!
When can we do it again?

Unit 3: Let's Connect!

Jane and Wade *page 1*

to use with *Kate's Game* **WORD COUNT: 89**

DECODABLE WORDS
Target Phonics Element
long /ā/a_e
came, Dave, Gale, Hale, Jane, Jane's, late, name, Shane, Tate, Wade
Words Using Previously Taught Skills
a, asked, at, best, big, but, class, did, dog, end, fish, frog, fun, get, got, his, in, is, it, it's, jumped, just, Miss, pet, tank, then, up, with, yelled

HIGH-FREQUENCY WORDS
away, late, school, today, way, why
Review: have, he, said, show, the, to, too, was, what, where

STORY WORD
snake

Slap Hello *page 7*

to use with *Kids Can Help* **WORD COUNT: 98**

DECODABLE WORDS
Target Phonics Element
s blend /sl/sl-
slap
s blend /sn/sn-
snap
s blend /sp/sp
spend, clasp
s blend /st/st-
stand, step, stop

Words Using Previously Taught Skills
a, and, backs, big, but, can, chat, clap, get, Gramps, grin, hand, hands, has, hats, hug, hugs, just, kiss, let's, men, Mom, not, off, pals, pats, peck, quick, shake, tell, then, Tim, up, wave, will, with

HIGH-FREQUENCY WORDS
all, could, hello, oh, pull, walk
Review: little, me, no, the, they, to, ways, we, what

CONCEPT WORD
time

Such a Grand Day! *page 13*

to use with *Short Shadows, Long Shadows*   **WORD COUNT: 128**

DECODABLE WORDS
Target Phonics Elements
 digraph /ch/ch
  chat, check, chess, chips; bunch, lunch, munch, sandwich, such, which
 digraph /ch/-tch
  batch, catch, pitch
 digraph /hw/wh-
  when, which, whip
Words Using Previously Taught Skills
a, and, at, baked, bed, big, bun, buns, bus, came, can, case, cats, class, dogs, don't, fed, fish, fresh, fun, game, get, grab, grand, grin, had, hot, I, in, is, just, kids, late, let's, on, pal, pet, pets, pick, pink, red, sets, six, sun, take, them, then, up, west, will, wish, with, yum,

HIGH-FREQUENCY WORDS
boy, care, girl, people, together, when, water
Review: be, for, of, one, play, see, some, the, today

CONCEPT WORDS
day, stretch

HIGH-FREQUENCY WORDS
call, funny, how, more, so, there
Review: for, here, looking, see, the, to, we

STORY WORD
photos

Review   **WORD COUNT: 108**

DECODABLE WORDS
Review Target Phonics Elements
long /ā/*a_e*
date, game, games, gaze, make, plate, take
***s* blends**
past, smile, spot, stand, step
digraphs /ch/*ch, -tch*
chat, lunch, such
catch, pitch
digraph /hw/*wh-*
whack, when
long /ī/*i_e*
bike, ride, smile, time
blend /str/*str-*
stretch, striped
Words Using Previously Taught Skills
a, and, as, at, back, band, big, can, clap, flags, fun, get, I, in, is, it, it's, let's, off, on, pals, think, the, this, up, with, yell

HIGH-FREQUENCY WORDS
Review: again, do, for, help, how, many, my, out, play, some, together, they, was, we, you

CONCEPT WORDS
ball, marching

44